Here's a photo of me.

My name is _____

My birthday is _____

My parents' names are

_____

_____

My brothers and sisters are

_____

_____

_____

Our pets are

_____

Here's a family photo.

KINDERGARTEN

Here's a photo of me
on my first day of Kindergarten!

I started Kindergarten now that

I am _____ years old!

Here is how I write my name: _____

I am _____ inches tall.

I go to school on these days of the week:

_____

in the: ☐ morning   ☐ afternoon   ☐ all day

The name of my school is _____

_____

My favorite thing about it is _____

_____

_____

My teacher's name is _____

and (s)he is really _____

At school, I am very:

- ☐ social
- ☐ energetic
- ☐ happy
- ☐ shy
- ☐ quiet
- ☐ nervous
- ☐ curious
- ☐ outspoken
- ☐ creative
- ☐ thoughtful

Some of my friends are:

_____

_____

_____

_____

Here's a photo of me and a Kindergarten pal!

My Kindergarten class ☐ does ☐ does not have a classroom pet.

It's a(n) _____

Its name is _____

ANIMAL ART!

Create a drawing of your
classroom pet or your favorite animal.

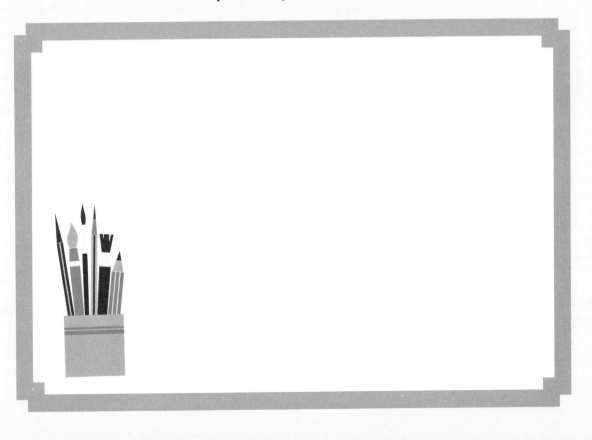

A FEW OF MY FAVORITE THINGS

My favorite snack is _____

My favorite stuffed animal is _____

My favorite bedtime story is _____

_____

My favorite song is _____

My favorite movie is _____

Here's a photo of me with
one of my favorite things!

CREATIVE IN CLASS

Attach a favorite piece of
artwork you created in Kindergarten.

MEMORY LANE

Use this space to post some of your favorite photos of Kindergarten memories.

FIRST GRADE

Here's a photo of me
on my first day of first grade!

I ☐ did ☐ did not pick out my own outfit for the
first day of school!

THIS YEAR...

I made new friends! My favorite thing about my friends is

_____

_____

Here are some of their names:

_____

_____

_____

This is a
drawing of
me with
a friend!

This is how I write my name as a first grader:

_____

This is how I write my teacher's name:

_____

My favorite thing about my first grade classroom is

_____

_____

_____

_____

My favorite part of the day is _____

_____

_____

_____

On the first day of first grade, I am _____

inches tall and _____ years old.

On the last day of first grade, I am _____

inches tall and _____ years old.

What can I do as a first grader?

(Check each box and see what you've learned during the year!)

I can...

First Day of First Grade   Last Day of First Grade

☐   read a book!   ☐

☐   write a sentence!   ☐

☐   work on the computer!   ☐

☐   play an instrument!   ☐

☐   add and subtract!   ☐

☐   tie my shoes!   ☐

☐   _____   ☐

(Choose your own skill!)

After school, I like to _____

_____

_____

As a special treat, my parents will let me

_____

_____

If I need help with my schoolwork,

I usually ask _____

_____

My favorite part about the weekend is

_____

_____

_____

Here's a look at some of my schoolwork from first grade!

SECOND GRADE

Here's a photo of
me in my classroom!

This is how I write my name as a second grader:

_____

This is how I write my teacher's name: _____

_____

My teacher is really _____

Here's a drawing of one of my favorite things!

I also really like _____

_____

My favorite thing to do after school is _____

_____

My favorite thing to do on the weekend is _____

_____

Here's a sample of some of my second grade schoolwork!

At school, I sit at

☐ my own desk!   ☐ a table with my classmates!

My favorite subjects are:

☐ math   ☐ recess

☐ reading   ☐ art

☐ writing   ☐ music

☐ science   ☐ computer class

☐ social studies

My school day starts at

____ : ____ and ends at ____ : ____

I get to school by

☐ a school bus!   ☐ a car!   ☐ walking!

☐ _____ drives me!

This year, I turned _____ years old.

On my birthday, I _____

_____

My favorite birthday present was _____

_____

Next year on my birthday, I would like to _____

_____

My teacher ☐ does ☐ does not celebrate our

birthdays in the classroom!

Here's a drawing of me on my birthday!

ARTISTIC FLAIR!

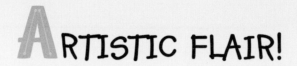

Draw a picture of anything you like!

THIRD GRADE

This year, I am _____ feet/inches tall, and _____ years old.

I am

☐ shorter ☐ taller

than most of my classmates!

Here's a photo of me on my first day of third grade!

The name of my school is _____

_____

and my teacher's name is _____

I ☐ do ☐ do not have a lot of the same classmates from second grade!

ACTIVITY TIME!

Here are some things that I do at school:
(Check all that apply and feel free to add other activities not listed here!)

☐ computer time   ☐ science projects

☐ art class   ☐ math problems

☐ gym   ☐ _____

☐ reading   ☐ _____

☐ writing   ☐ _____

My favorite subject is _____ because

_____

_____

I would like to get better at this subject:

_____

Here are the names of my best friends!

_____   _____

_____   _____

_____   _____

Together, my friends and I like to _____

_____

_____

Here's a photo of me and a friend!

Here's a sample of my third grade schoolwork!

I like third grade ☐ more ☐ less than second grade.

Why? _____

_____

_____

This year, I got really good at _____

_____

My family was really proud of me when

_____

_____

_____

A really funny moment was when _____

_____

_____

_____

_____

STAR POWER!

Here's a photo of me in a
third grade assembly/play/
musical or other fun event!

FOURTH GRADE

Here is my signature! _____

This year, I am _____ feet _____ inches tall

and _____ years old.

My school ☐ does ☐ does not have a mascot!

It is a _____

Here's a photo of
me in fourth grade!

As a fourth grader, I'm now really good at _____

_____

but I'd like to be better at _____

_____

I want to be a(n) _____

when I grow up because _____

_____

I also want to:

- ☐ graduate from college
- ☐ travel around the world
- ☐ eat ice cream for dinner
- ☐ help the environment
- ☐ make lots of friends

- ☐ drive a fast car
- ☐ other: _____

_____

Draw a picture of yourself as an adult!

Here's a sample of my fourth grade schoolwork!

This is my favorite book we read in class:

_____

READING   It was about _____

_____

_____

_____

This is my favorite movie: _____

_____

My favorite food: _____

_____

My favorite color: _____

My favorite family memory: _____

_____

_____

_____

_____

My class ☐ did ☐ did not take field trips this year!

We went to _____

_____

and we learned about _____

_____

_____

I ☐ do ☐ do not like field trip days because

_____

Here's a photo of me on a trip!

FIFTH GRADE

Here's my fifth grade signature:

_____

I am _____ feet _____ inches tall and

_____ years old.

My teacher's name is _____

My best friend's name is _____

Here are some things I like to do with my friends:

☐ watch movies   ☐ play sports   ☐ make jokes

☐ read books   ☐ eat lunch   ☐ homework

☐ go shopping   ☐ sit and talk   ☐ other:

_____

MEMORY LANE

Here are some photos of me and my friends from fifth grade.

Class Time!

My classroom is really _____

_____

My desk is _____

_____

My favorite thing about fifth grade is _____

_____

I ☐ do ☐ do not stay in the same classroom all day.

I ☐ do ☐ do not have my own locker.

My class visited these places on field trips this year:

_____   _____

_____   _____

_____   _____

Down Time

On the weekend, I like to:

☐ sleep in

☐ hang out with friends

☐ go to the movies

☐ go out to eat

☐ spend time with my family

☐ go on trips

☐ catch up on homework

☐ watch TV

☐ read a book

☐ other: _____

My favorite thing to do after school is

_____

_____

_____

My bedtime is _____

Here's a sample of my fifth grade schoolwork!

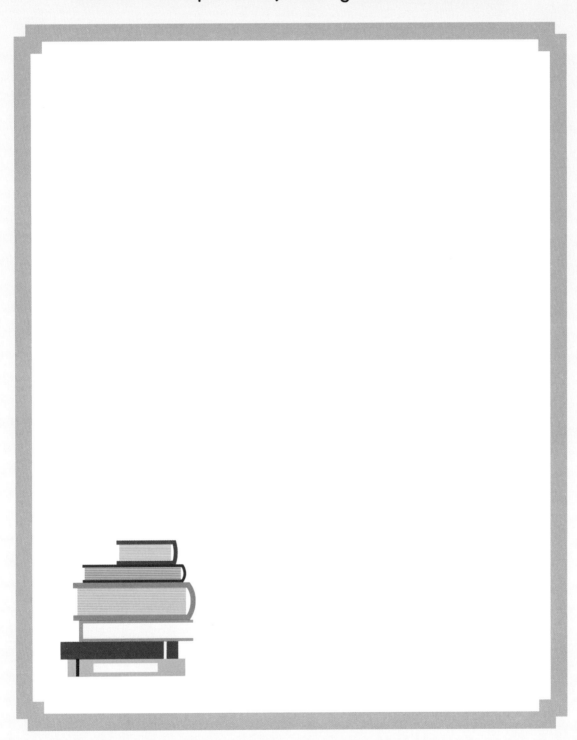

For my birthday this year, I _____

_____

_____

My favorite holiday is _____

_____

My family and I celebrate by

_____

_____

_____

We [ ] do [ ] do not celebrate this holiday in

my classroom!

If I could wish for one thing, it would be

_____

_____

_____

SIXTH GRADE

Here's a photo of me in sixth grade!

This year, I [ ] do [ ] do not stay in the same classroom all day.

These are my favorite subjects this year:

_____

_____

_____

_____

_____

I use a [ ] backpack [ ] messenger bag

[ ] rolling tote [ ] other: _____ to carry my

books to and from school!

IN THE CLUB!

Here's a list of clubs I'm in:

_____   _____

_____   _____

_____   _____

_____   _____

Here's a photo of
a club or team activity!

Here's a sample of a test I took in sixth grade!

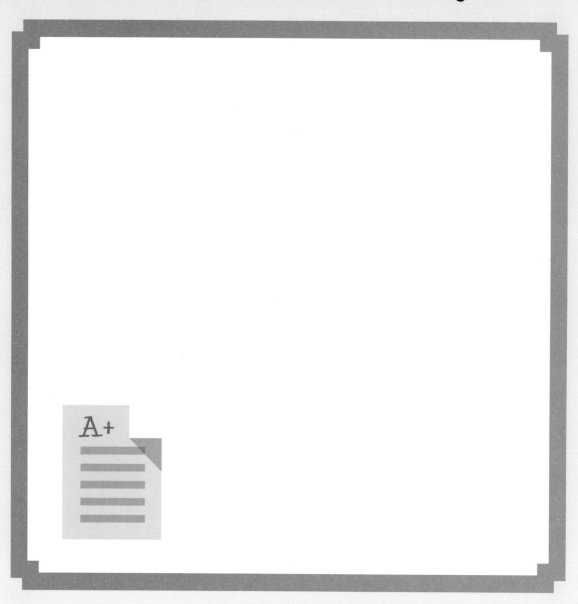

I thought this test was really

☐ easy   ☐ hard   ☐ fair

Food for Thought!

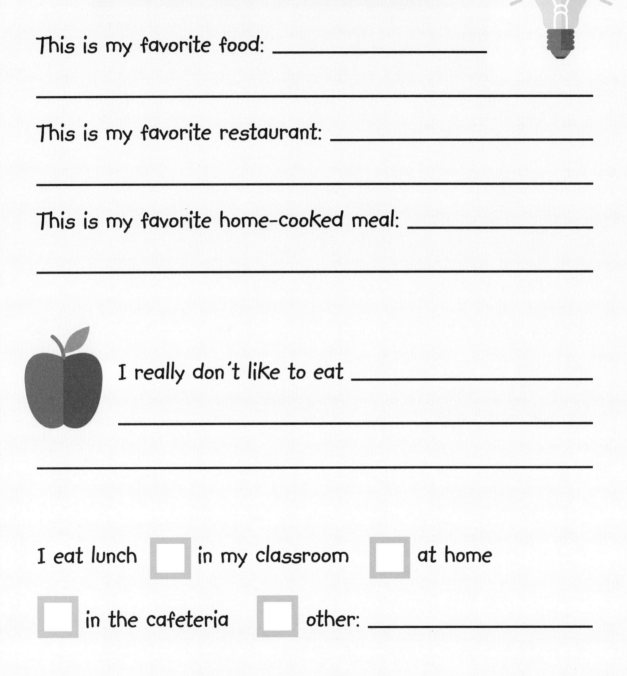

This is my favorite food: _____

_____

This is my favorite restaurant: _____

_____

This is my favorite home-cooked meal: _____

_____

I really don't like to eat _____

_____

_____

I eat lunch ☐ in my classroom ☐ at home

☐ in the cafeteria ☐ other: _____

This year, I worked on these projects:

_____

_____

_____

With these classmates:

_____   _____

_____   _____

_____   _____

My favorite thing about group projects is _____

_____

_____

_____

_____

I prefer to work alone on these subjects:

_____

_____

SEVENTH GRADE

Here's my most professional signature:

_____

This year, I am _____ years old and _____

feet _____ inches tall.

I ☐ am ☐ am not

taller than some of my

adult relatives and am

☐ shorter ☐ taller

than most of my friends!

Here's a seventh
grade photo of me!

SLICE OF SOCIAL LIFE!

Some of my best friends are:

_____   _____

_____   _____

_____   _____

When we get together, we are really:

☐ goofy   ☐ studious   ☐ loud

☐ respectful   ☐ creative   ☐ quiet

☐ adventurous

☐ diverse

☐ laid back   Here's a photo of
                           me with a friend!

☐ other:

_____

TEAM SPIRIT!

Here's a list of the groups, clubs, sports or performances
I participated in this year:

_____   _____

_____   _____

_____   _____

_____   _____

Here's a photo of me
on the field or on the stage!

Here's a sample of my 7th grade schoolwork!

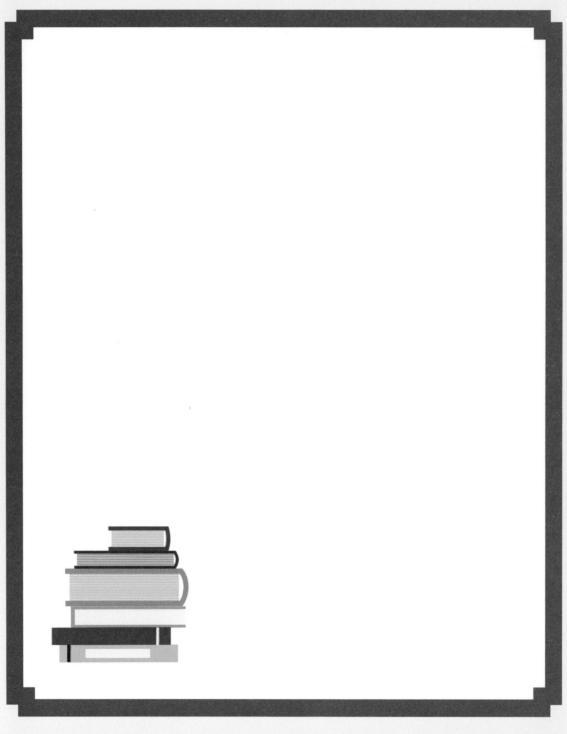

I ☐ do ☐ do not have a cell phone.

I use it mostly to _____

_____

I ☐ do ☐ do not have my own computer.

My favorite way to use technology is

_____

_____

_____

and I use it to help with schoolwork by _____

_____

_____

My favorite web site is

_____

My favorite seventh grade teacher is _____

_____

_____

My favorite subject is _____

_____

I think I improved the most in this subject:

_____

Next year I'd like to be even better at _____

_____

_____

A hidden talent I have is _____

_____

_____

EIGHTH GRADE

My last year of middle school! I am _____ feet _____ inches tall, and _____ years old.

I am very excited about having this class:

_____

_____

Here's a photo of me with my friend(s)!

with this friend: _____

My favorite teachers are _____

_____

I travel to and from school by _____

_____

This year, I am in these clubs and on these teams:

_____

_____

_____

_____

_____

Here are some big competitions or games I'm looking

forward to this year:

_____

_____

_____

_____

_____

My best friends are:

_____   _____

_____   _____

_____   _____

They ☐ do ☐ do not all go to school with me.

On the weekends, you can find us _____

_____

_____

After school, I'm usually _____

_____

My favorite thing to do with my family is _____

_____

_____

My parents ☐ do ☐ do not help me with a lot of

my schoolwork!

Here's a sample of a test I took in eighth grade!

A+

This is from a subject I thought was really
☐ challenging   ☐ straightforward

Here are some favorites from this year!

Book: _____

_____

Movie: _____

_____

Band: _____

_____

Song: _____

_____

Memory with friends: _____

_____

_____

Memory with family: _____

_____

_____

Class/Subject: _____

Here's my favorite overall thing about middle school:

_____

_____

Here's what I'm most looking forward to

about high school: _____

_____

_____

The name of the high school I'm going to is

_____

Their mascot is _____

I hope I improve in these subjects: _____

_____

I hope I continue to shine in these subjects:

_____

_____

LOOKING BACK

I did the best academically in this year: _____

_____

I had the most fun this year: _____

My parent(s) were super proud of me when _____

_____

A teacher I remember especially fondly is _____

_____ because _____

_____

I couldn't have done it without these friends: _____

_____

My favorite special event was _____

I have really great memories of this holiday: _____

_____

I was most proud of myself when _____

_____

LOOKING FORWARD

I think high school is going to be _____

When I grow up, I would like to be a(n) _____

_____

I'd love to live in this city: _____

I'd like to travel to _____

_____

For a pet, I hope to someday have a(n) _____

_____ and I'll name it _____

Here are some causes I hope to volunteer for:

_____   _____

_____   _____

I think the future will be really _____

_____